With love.
Auntie Kerrie
x

Written by Rachel Lawrence
Illustrated by Andrea Evans

First published by Parragon in 2010

Parragon
Queen Street House
4 Queen Street
Bath BA1 1HE, UK

ISBN 978-1-4075-8817-9

Printed in China

My Baby Book

PaRragon

Bath · New York · Singapore · Hong Kong · Cologne · Delhi · Melbourne

moments we don't want to forget...

this is a picture of me at...................weeks

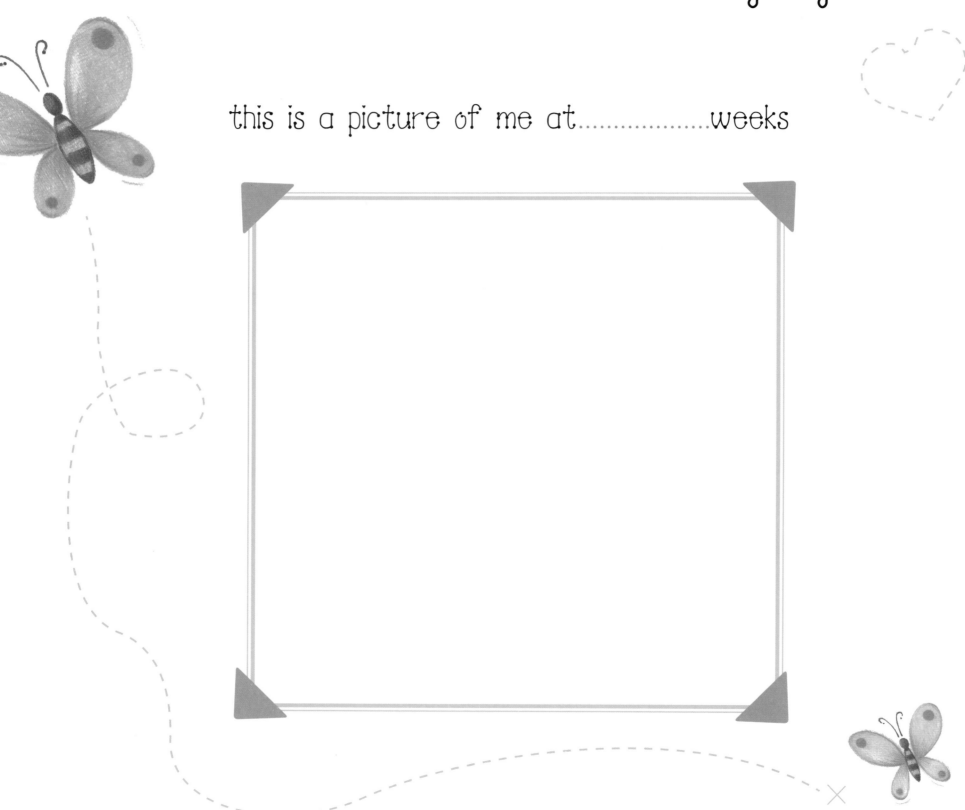

mummy's food cravings during pregnancy

....

how the news of my arrival was celebrated

....

we received the following gifts

....

what mummy was doing on the day I was born

....

mummy and daddy

mummy's name ....

mummy's birth date ....

mummy's place of birth ....

mummy's horoscope ....

mummy's hair colour ....

mummy's eye colour ....

mummy's job ....

mummy's hobbies ....

daddy's name ....

daddy's birth date ....

daddy's place of birth ....

daddy's horoscope ....

daddy's hair colour ....

daddy's eye colour ....

daddy's job ....

daddy's hobbies ....

my name

my name is ....

what my name means ....

....

the reason my name was chosen ....

....

my mummy and daddy might have called me ....

....

my family tree

great grandparents	great grandparents	great grandparents	great grandparents
....	....	....	....
....	....	....	....

granddad	grandma	granddad	grandma
....	....	....	....

aunts/uncles	mummy	daddy	aunts/uncles
....			....
....			....

me

brothers			sisters
....	....		....
....			....

my birth

I was born on ....

at this time ....

at ....

I weighed ....

I was .... long

my hair was ....

people at the birth ....

my first visitors were ....

here is a picture of me when I was born

cute cheeks

cute nose

cute eyes

cute toes!

Rock-a-bye, Baby

Rock-a-bye, baby,
on the treetop,
When the wind blows,
the cradle will rock;

When the bough breaks,
the cradle will fall,
Down will come baby,
cradle and all.

my first days at home

I came home on ....

I lived at ....

....

my first visitors at home ....

gifts I received ....

....

....

....

how I slept in my first week ....

how mummy and daddy felt in the first week

....

....

a photo of me in my first few days

teeny

tiny

and

totally

cute!

date taken ....

Incy Wincy Spider

Incy Wincy spider
climbing up the spout,
Down came the rain
and washed poor Incy out.
Out came the sun,
and dried up all the rain,
Incy Wincy spider
climbed up the spout again.

If You're Happy
and You Know it

If you're happy and you know it,
Clap your hands.
If you're happy and you know it,
Clap your hands.
If you're happy and you know it,
And you really want to show it,
If you're happy and you know it,
Clap your hands.

bathtime

the first time I had a bath in the big bath

....

my favourite bathtime toys

....

here is a photo of me in the bath

bathtime
is so
much fun!

date taken

....

bedtime

about my cot ....

I moved to a big bed ....

I first slept through the night ....

my favourite toys ....

my favourite books ....

my favourite nursery rhymes ....

....

Twinkle, Twinkle, Little Star

Twinkle, twinkle, little star,
How I wonder what you are!
Up above the world so high,
Like a diamond in the sky.

When the blazing sun is gone,
When he nothing shines upon,
Then you show your little light,
Twinkle, twinkle all the night.

Then the traveller in the dark —
Thanks you for your tiny spark,
He could not see which way to go,
If you did not twinkle so.

In the dark blue sky you keep,
And often through my curtains peep,
For you never shut your eye,
'Till the sun is in the sky.

As your bright and tiny spark,
Lights the traveller in the dark
Though I know not what you are,
Twinkle, twinkle, little star.

Jane Taylor

my footprint

date taken ....

my handprint

date taken ....

 I'm so new!

Jack and Jill

Jack and Jill went up the hill,
To fetch a pail of water;
Jack fell down and broke his crown,
And Jill came tumbling after.

Then Jack got up and home did trot,
As fast as he could caper;
He went to bed, to mend his head,
With vinegar and brown paper.

first moves

I first rolled over ....

I sat up all by myself ....

I crawled ....

I took my very first steps ....

a photo of me
on the move

look who's
crawling!

date taken

....

first food

first food ....

I first drank from a cup ....

favourite fruit purees ....

foods I like ....

foods I dislike ....

my special treats ....

I first sat in a high chair ....

Lavender's Blue

Lavender's blue, dilly, dilly,
Lavender's green;
When I am king, dilly, dilly,
You shall be queen.

Hey Diddle Diddle

Hey diddle diddle, the cat and the fiddle,
The cow jumped over the moon.
The little dog laughed to see such fun,
And the dish ran away with the spoon!

first trips and outings

my first holiday or trip was to ....

I went with...

what I loved ....

what I hated ....

my first outing on a train or bus ....

here is a photo of me on my holiday

date taken ....

bon voyage!

Hickory Dickory Dock

Hickory dickory dock,
The mouse ran up the clock.
The clock struck one,
The mouse ran down,
Hickory dickory dock.

Ring-a-Ring o' Roses

Ring-a-ring o'roses,
A pocket full of posies.
A-tishoo! A-tishoo!
We all fall down.

1 month

things I can do now ....

....

funny things I do ....

....

how I've been sleeping ....

....

I weigh ....

I'm .... long

this is me at one month

this is me and my family

it runs in
the family

months

new things I can do ....

....

funny sounds I make ....

....

I smile when ....

my favourite nursery rhymes ....

....

I weigh ....

I'm .... long

I'm awake
a lot more
now!

here I am at two months

 tiny yawns and sleepy sighs,
nursery rhymes and lullabies.

Humpty Dumpty

Humpty Dumpty sat on a wall,
Humpty Dumpty had a great fall;
All the king's horses and all the king's men
Couldn't put Humpty together again!

Rain, Rain, Go Away

Rain, rain, go away,
Come again another day.
Little Jenny wants to play.

3 months

things I can do ....

....

I love these toys and games ....

....

funny things I do ....

....

I weigh ....

I am .... long

this is me at three months

 growing cuter
by the day!

4 months

I like toys that make loud noises!

new things I can do now ....

....

baby groups I go to ....

....

new places I've been to ....

....

I weigh ....

I am .... long

this is me at four months

this is a photo of me sleeping

snug as
a bug in
a hug!

Little Miss Muffet

Little Miss Muffet
Sat on a tuffet,
Eating her curds and whey;
Along came a spider,
Who sat down beside her
And frightened Miss Muffet away.

Row, Row, Row Your Boat

Row, row, row your boat
Gently down the stream.
Merrily, merrily, merrily, merrily,
Life is but a dream.

5 months

things I can do at five months ....

....

funny things I do ....

....

my favourite things to hug ....

....

I weigh ....

I am .... long

I love bouncing up and down!

here I am at five months!

a new little
hand to hold

months

My favourite
game is
'peek-a-boo'

new things I can do ....

....

favourite bathtime toys ....

....

how I've been sleeping ....

....

my friends ....

I weigh ....

I am .... long

I'm six months old now!

cute as
a button

This Little Piggy

(Pretend each of the child's
toes is a little piggy.
Begin with the biggest toe and finish
by tickling under the child's foot.)

This little piggy went to market,
This little piggy stayed home,
This little piggy had roast beef,
This little piggy had none,
And this little piggy cried,
"Wee, wee, wee!"
All the way home.

7 months

new things I can do ....

....

my favourite toys ....

....

places I've been to ....

....

I weigh ....

I'm .... long

I love pop-up toys and other surprises!

this is me at seven months

this is a photo of me with my favourite toy

kisses and
hugs
sent from
above

months

new things I can do ....

....

my friends are ....

....

My favourite toy/book is ....

....

I weigh ....

I am .... long

a photo of me at eight months

a new little
heart to love

Little Bo-Peep

Little Bo-Peep has lost her sheep,
And doesn't know where to find them;
Leave them alone,
and they'll come home,
Wagging their tails behind them.

Mary Had a Little Lamb

Mary had a little lamb,
Its fleece was white as snow;
And everywhere that Mary went
The lamb was sure to go.
It followed her to school one day,
Which was against the rules;
It made the children laugh and play
To see a lamb at school.

months

new things I can do ....

....

cute things I do ....

....

new foods I've eaten ....

....

I weigh ....

I am .... long

I love building blocks!

this is me at nine months!

 growing cuter
by the day

10 months

things I can do at ten months...

....

my favourite activity ....

....

words I understand ....

....

foods I like ....

I weigh ....

I am .... long

this is me at ten months

this is a photo of me being a messy eater!

little arms to
hold tight,
little cheeks
to kiss good
night!

Five Little Ducks

Five little ducks went swimming one day,
Over the hills and far away.
Mother Duck said, "Quack, quack, quack, quack,"
But only four little ducks came back.

Four little ducks went swimming one day,
Over the hills and far away.
Mother Duck said, "Quack, quack, quack, quack,"
But only three little ducks came back.

Three little ducks went swimming one day,
Over the hills and far away.
Mother Duck said, "Quack, quack, quack, quack,"
But only two little ducks came back.

Two little ducks went swimming one day,
Over the hills and far away.
Mother Duck said, "Quack, quack, quack, quack,"
But only one little duck came back.

One little duck went swimming one day,
Over the hills and far away.
Mother Duck said, "Quack, quack, quack, quack,"
But none of the five little ducks came back.

Mother Duck went swimming one day,
Over the hills and far away.
Mother Duck said, "Quack, quack, quack, quack,"
And five little ducks came swimming back.

months

new things I can do ....

....

my favourite first words ....

....

I have .... teeth

I weigh ....

I'm .... long

I'm getting mobile!

I'm eleven months old!

here I am on the move

sweetness is hereditary

12 months

I can say my first words!

new things I can do ....

....

words I can say now ....

....

funny things I do ....

....

I weigh ....

I am .... long

a photo of me at twelve months

it's the little things
that matter most

my first birthday

what I did ....

....

who came to see me ....

....

gifts I received ....

happy 1st birthday

....

food I ate ....

a photo of me on my first birthday

my first Christmas

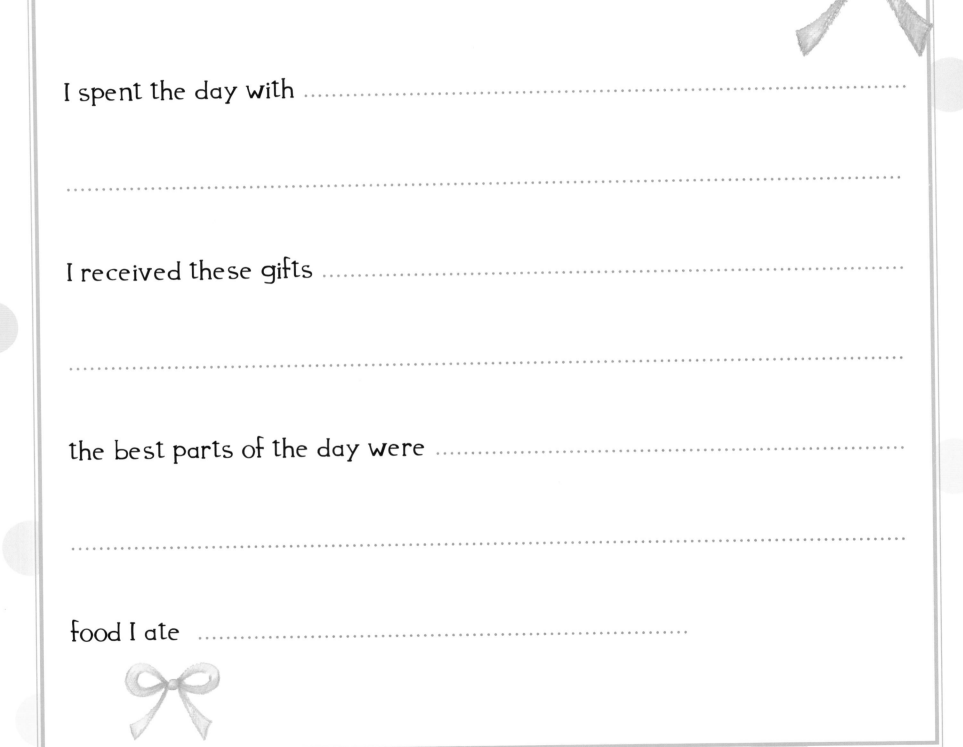

I spent the day with ....

....

I received these gifts ....

....

the best parts of the day were ....

....

food I ate ....

this is me on my first Christmas day!

date taken ....

Sing a Song of Sixpence

Sing a song of sixpence
A pocket full of rye;
Four and twenty blackbirds
Baked in a pie.
When the pie was opened
The birds began to sing;
Now wasn't that a dainty dish
To set before the king?

The king was in his counting house,
Counting out his money;
The queen was in the parlour
Eating bread and honey.
The maid was in the garden,
Hanging out the clothes,
When down came a blackbird
And pecked off her nose!

The Queen of Hearts

The Queen of Hearts, she made some tarts,
All on a summer's day.
The Knave of Hearts, he stole the tarts,
And took them clean away.

The King of Hearts, called for the tarts,
And beat the Knave full sore.
The Knave of Hearts, brought back the tarts
And vowed he'd steal no more.

my naming day

I spent the day with ....

....

gifts I received ....

....

....

the best parts of the day were ....

....

....

this is me on my naming day

date taken ....

One, Two, Buckle my Shoe

One, two, buckle my shoe;

Three, four, knock at the door;

Five, six, pick up sticks;

Seven, eight, lay them straight;

Nine, ten, a big fat hen;

Eleven, twelve, dig and delve;

Thirteen, fourteen, maids a-courting;

Fifteen, sixteen, maids in the kitchen;

Seventeen, eighteen, maids in waiting;

Nineteen, twenty, my plate's empty!

visits to the doctor

my doctor is ....

....

....

immunizations ....

....

....

....

....

....

....

allergies ....

....

....

....

illnesses ....

....

....

....

....

....

Round and Round the Garden

Round and round the garden,
Round and round the garden
Like a teddy bear;
(Draw a circle on the palm of your
baby's hand with your finger)

One step, two steps,
(Walk your fingers up your baby's arm)

Tickle you under there!
(Tickle baby under the arm)

Teddy Bear, Teddy Bear

Teddy bear, teddy bear,
　　Touch the ground.
Teddy bear, teddy bear,
　　Turn around.

　　　　　　Teddy bear, teddy bear,
　　　　　　　　Walk upstairs.
　　　　　　Teddy bear, teddy bear,
　　　　　　　　Say your prayers.

Teddy bear, teddy bear,
　　Turn out the light.
Teddy bear, teddy bear,
　　Say goodnight.

a year in pictures

other special things about me...